AT GRANDMOTHER'S
Part 2
To Bed

Jan Joss

illustrated by
Mary Ann Lumm

JOURNEY BOOKS

© 1998 Journey Books
Published by Bob Jones University Press
Greenville, SC 29614
ISBN 0-89084-987-0

You are yellow, very yellow.

You are just like Grandmother's kitten.

You are wet, very wet.

You are just like Grandmother's duck.

3

You are big, very big.

You are just like Grandmother's pig.

4

"Here is a puppy for you, Jim."

You are sad, very sad.

You are just like
  Grandmother's puppy.

"You are good, very good,
and I love You."

6

I cannot rest.

What can I do?

"Here is a kitten for you, Grandmother."

I cannot rest.

What can I do?

9

"Here is a duck for you, Grandmother."

"And here is a pig for you, Grandmother."

"Here is a puppy for you, Grandmother."

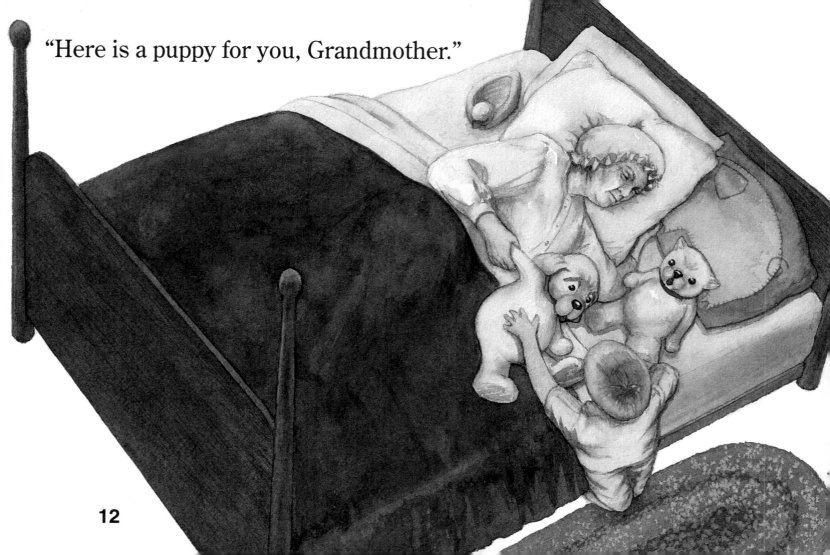

I still cannot rest!

What can I do?

13

"Good night, Kitten.

Good night, Duck.

Good night, Pig.

Good night, Puppy.

Good night, Grandmother."

"Good night, Jim."

Can a vest rest?

must	rest	kit
trust	vest	sit
just	best	quit

Service words:

do what

Enrichment words:

good like love night puppy yellow

Structural words:

cannot grandmother kitten